ASIAPAC COMIC SERIES

The Sayings of LIE ZI

The Taoist who rides in the wind

Edited & illustrated by
Tsai Chih Chung
Translated by
Koh Kok Kiang

ASIAPAC . SINGAPORE

Publisher
ASIAPAC BOOKS & EDUCATIONAL AIDS (S) PTE LTD
2 Leng Kee Road
#02-08 Thye Hong Centre
Singapore 0315
Tel: 475 1777
Fax: 479 6366

First published December 1991

ISBN 9971-985-67-5

Cover design by
Marked Point Design Pte Ltd
Typeset by
Quaser Technology Pte Ltd
Printed in Singapore by
Loi Printing Pte Ltd

Publisher's Note

Following the Sayings of Lao Zi and Zhuang Zi, we are pleased to present to you yet another Taoist classic, *The Sayings of Lie Zi*.

Lie Zi, though a half-legendary figure, ranks among the most famous Taoist sages. And the book which bears his name, *The Book of Lie Zi*, is one of the most important and intelligible of the Taoist classics.

It is a collection of sayings, stories on such universal themes as the joy of living, reconciliation with death, the value of spontaneity, the identity of dream and reality, the limitation of human knowledge, the relativity of standards of conduct, and the role of unpredictable and chance events.

We feel honoured to have well-known Taiwanese cartoonist Tsai Chih Chung's permission to the translation right to his bestselling comics. We would like also to take this opportunity to thank the translator and typesetter for putting in their best effort in the production of this series.

Other Titles in Asiapac Comic Series

About the Editor/Illustrator

Tsai Chih Chung was born in 1948 in Chang Hwa County of Taiwan. He began drawing cartoon strips at the age of 17 and worked as Art Director for Kuang Chi Programme Service in 1971. He founded the Far East Animation Production Company and the Dragon Cartoon Production Company in 1976, where he produced two cartoon films entitled *Old Master Q* and *Shao Lin Temple*.

Tsai Chih Chung first got his four-box comics published in newspapers and magazines in 1983. His funny comic characters such as the Drunken Swordsman, Fat Dragon, One-eyed Marshal and Bold Supersleuth have been serialized in newspapers in Singapore, Malaysia, Taiwan, Hong Kong, Japan, Europe, and the United States.

He was voted one of the Ten Outstanding Young People of Taiwan in 1985 and was acclaimed by the media and the academic circle in Taiwan.

The comic book *The Sayings of Zhuang Zi* was published in 1986 and marked a milestone in Tsai's career. Within two years, *Zhuang Zi* went into more than 70 reprints in Taiwan and 15 in Hong Kong and has to-date sold over one million copies.

In 1987, Tsai Chih Chung published *The Sayings of Lao Zi*, *The Sayings of Confucius* and two books based on Zen. Since then, he has published more than 20 titles, out of which 10 are about ancient Chinese thinkers and the rest based on historical and literary classics. All these books topped the bestsellers' list at one time or another. They have been translated into other languages such as Japanese, Korean, Thai. Asiapac is the publisher for the English version of these comics.

Tsai Chih Chung can be said to be the pioneer in the art of visualizing Chinese literature and philosophy by way of comics.

Introduction

Taoism is the greatest philosophical tradition of China after Confucianism. Taoism represents everything which is spontaneous, imaginative, private and unconventional in Chinese society; Confucianism represents everything which is controlled, prosaic, public and respectable. The division runs through the whole of Chinese civilization.

However, the two philosophical traditions have the same goal - order in living. The Way of Confucianism is primarily a system of government and moral code, mastered by study, thought and discipline. Man is the centre of the universe, "making a trinity with heaven and earth". Heaven is a vaguely personal power, ruling as the Emperor (the Son of Heaven) rules men. Destiny is the "decree of heaven". The world order is a counterpart of the social order.

For Taoists, on the other hand, man occupies the humble position of the tiny figures in a Chinese landscape painting, and lives rightly by bringing himself in accord with a Way that does not favour his ambitions, inclinations and moral principles. If he wishes to return to the Way, he must discard human knowledge, cease to make distinctions, refuse to impose his will and his principles on Nature, recover the spontaneity of the newborn child, and allow his actions to be as natural as the physical processes of Nature.

Although regarded as one of the most prominent Taoist sages, Lie Zi's existence is doubtful. It is not even clear when he is supposed to have lived. Some indications point to 600BC, others to 400BC. However, the book which bears his name appeared around AD300, and it is a collection of stories, brief sayings and essays grouped into eight chapters, each loosely organized around a single theme.

Compared to the occasionally abstruse passages of the works of Lao Zi and Zhuang Zi, the two most well-known Taoist figures, the Book of Lie Zi has the merit of being by far the most easily intelligible classics of Taoism.

But this is not to say that the Way expounded by Lie Zi is any less lofty. His ideal is a state of heightened perception and responsiveness in an undifferentiated world:

"My body is in accord with my mind, my mind with my energies, my energies with my spirit, my spirit with Nothing. Whenever the minutest existing thing or the faintest sound affects me, whether it is far away beyond the eight borderlands, or close at hand between my eyebrows and eyelashes, I am bound to know it. However, I do not know whether I perceived it with the seven holes in my head and four limbs, or knew it through my heart and belly and internal organs. It is simply self-knowing."

"Only then, when I had come to the end of everything inside me and outside me, my eyes became like my ears, my ears like my nose, my nose like my mouth; everything was the same. My mind was silent and my body had dissolved, my bones and flesh had melted into nothingness. I did not notice what my body leaned against and what my feet trod. I drifted with the wind East or West, like a leaf from a tree or a dry husk, and never knew whether it was the wind that rode me or I that rode the wind."

So far, there is only one complete translation in English of the Book of Lie Zi. It is entitled *Book of Lieh-tzu* by A.C.Graham (John Murray, 1960).

Koh Kok Kiang

About the translator

Koh Kok Kiang is a journalist by vocation and a quietist by inclination. He is a sub-editor with *The Straits Times* of Singapore. His interest in cultural topics and things of the mind started in his schooling years. It was his wish to discover the wisdom of the East that kindled his interest in Eastern philosophy. He is also the translator for *Book of Zen* and *Origins of Zen,* and co-translator for *The Sayings of Lao Zi,* in our Asiapac Comic Series.

Contents

Heaven's Gifts 天瑞 1

Three reasons to be happy 快乐的三个原因 2
Life is activity, death is rest 生为徭役 4
Will the sky fall down? 杞人忧天 7

The Yellow Emperor 黄帝 9

Lie Zi rides the wind 列子御风而行 10
The shaman meets his match 神巫的相术 13
Lie Zi's burden 列子惊惧 17
Beauty and ugliness 美与丑 19

King Mu of Zhou 周穆王 20

King Mu's journey of the spirit 周穆王神遊 21
Lao Cheng Zi learns the secret and sublime 老成子学幻 25
Lie Zi on dreams 列子说梦 27
Joy and sorrow 苦乐的真相 30
Dream or reality 是梦是真 32
Loss of memory 华子健忘症 34
Who is normal? 迷惘的是谁 36
Tricks of the mind 见物思情 37

Confucius 仲尼 39

Who is a sage? 圣人乎 40
The disciples' shortcomings 师者有兼才 42
The joy of travel 用心去玩 44

The Questions of Tang 汤问 45

The things of creation 长短、大小、高下 46
Moving the mountain 愚公移山 50
Kua Fu chases the sun 夸父逐日 52

Traditions and customs 异国奇俗 54
Spirit of the lute 师文学琴 55
Singing with heart and soul 绕梁三日 59
A friend after one's own heart 伯牙鼓琴 63
The sublime archer 不射的神箭 66
The art of the charioteer 泰豆心法 76
A son's vengeance 来丹报仇 78

Endeavour and Destiny 力命 82
Destiny 命 83
Clinging to life and shunning death 贪生怕死 84
Death is nothing to grieve over 死不足悲 86

Yang Zhu 杨朱 87
The emptiness of fame 名无实 实无名 89
Life is short 生暂来 死暂往 92
Life and death 生与死 94
Wealth and poverty are both harmful 贫害身、富累身 96
Madman or clever man? 狂人？达人？ 97
Living and dying 顺其生 顺其死 100
Not sacrificing a hair for the world 拔一毛以利天下 101
The great and the trifling 治大者不治细 103
Empty pursuits 寿、名、位、货 105
Simple-minded rustic 野人献曝 106

Explaining Conjunctions 说符 107
Self and shadow 持后的道理 108
Echo 影响 109
Aim of learning the Tao 学道的目的 110
Lie Zi learns archery 列子学射 111
Foolishness and wisdom 知贤而不自贤 112
Trying to outdo nature 不恃智巧 113
Foresight 先知的话 114
A question of timing 失时者亡 115

Attack and being attacked 我伐人 人亦伐我 117
The rain that does not last 骤雨不终日 118
Good luck and tough luck 幸与不幸 119
Horse sense 善相马者不知牝牡 120
The higher you go, the harder you fall 爵高官大禄厚 122
Death of two fools 理无常是 事无常非 123
The unlucky gambler 锋芒之害 126
Refusing a criminal's food 不食盗食 127
Past caring about death 士为不知己者死 128
Yang Bu beats the dog 杨布打狗 129
Life and immortality 知行分立 130
Charity or cruelty 恩过相补 131
The strong eating the weak 弱肉强食 132
Disgrace 耻 133
Empty wealth 钱 134
Evil designs 心中的善恶 135
Evil thoughts 心中的贼 136
Thoughts of rebellion 颐之忘 将何不忘哉 137
Tunnel vision 眼之所见 138

THE BOOK OF LIE ZI

The Taoist Who Rides The Wind

Among the classics of Taoism, the works of Lao Zi, Zhuang Zi and Lie Zi are said to be the most representative. Among them, The Book of Lie Zi is the most intelligible. Lie Zi's appeal was so widespread that in the forty years of his life in Zheng state, almost everyone knew his teachings although he lived in obscurity. Only the King knew nothing of his greatness.

He said:

To be born when you will be born, that's good fortune. To die when you will die, that's good fortune.

To be born and yet not cherish life, that's opposing heaven. Not to want to die when it's time to die, that's opposing heaven.

Heaven's Gifts

Three reasons to be happy
1
When Confucius was roaming on Taishan, he saw Rong Qiqi sitting on the roadside, singing as he strummed a lute.
2
3
May I know why you are so full of joy?
There are many things that give me joy...
4
Among the myriad things, mankind is the most noble, and I have the luck to be a human; that is my first joy.
5
Of the two sexes, men are given higher status than women, I have the luck to be a man; this is my second joy.
!

6
People are born and some live long and some die early. There are even those who die soon after birth. But I have already lived to ninety; this is my third joy.
7
For humans, a life of hardship is the norm and death is the end.
8
Abiding by the norm, awaiting my end, what is there to be concerned about?
9
Rong Qiqi is a person who knows how to face life.
Hardship, old age and death are regarded by humans as the bane of life, but Rong Qiqi accepts them as part and parcel of life. Thus, if you are able to see through something, you are in paradise, if not, you find yourself in hell.

Life is activity, death is rest
1
Confucius, while on his way to Wei kingdom, saw an old man named Lin Lei who was nearly a hundred years old. Lin put on his fur coat in the middle of spring, and went to pick up the grains dropped by the reapers, singing as he made his way through the fields.
2
This old man is an unusual person... Zi Kong, go talk to him and find out what makes him so happy.
Yes.
3
You are so old and yet you have to work so hard. Don't you find this a matter of regret?
What is there for me to regret?
4
What makes you so happy, picking up the grains and singing as you go?
The reason for my happiness is very simple.
5
The reason for my happiness all men share. But instead they worry over them. It is because I took no pains learning to behave when I was young, and never strove to make my mark when I grew up, that I have been able to live so long.

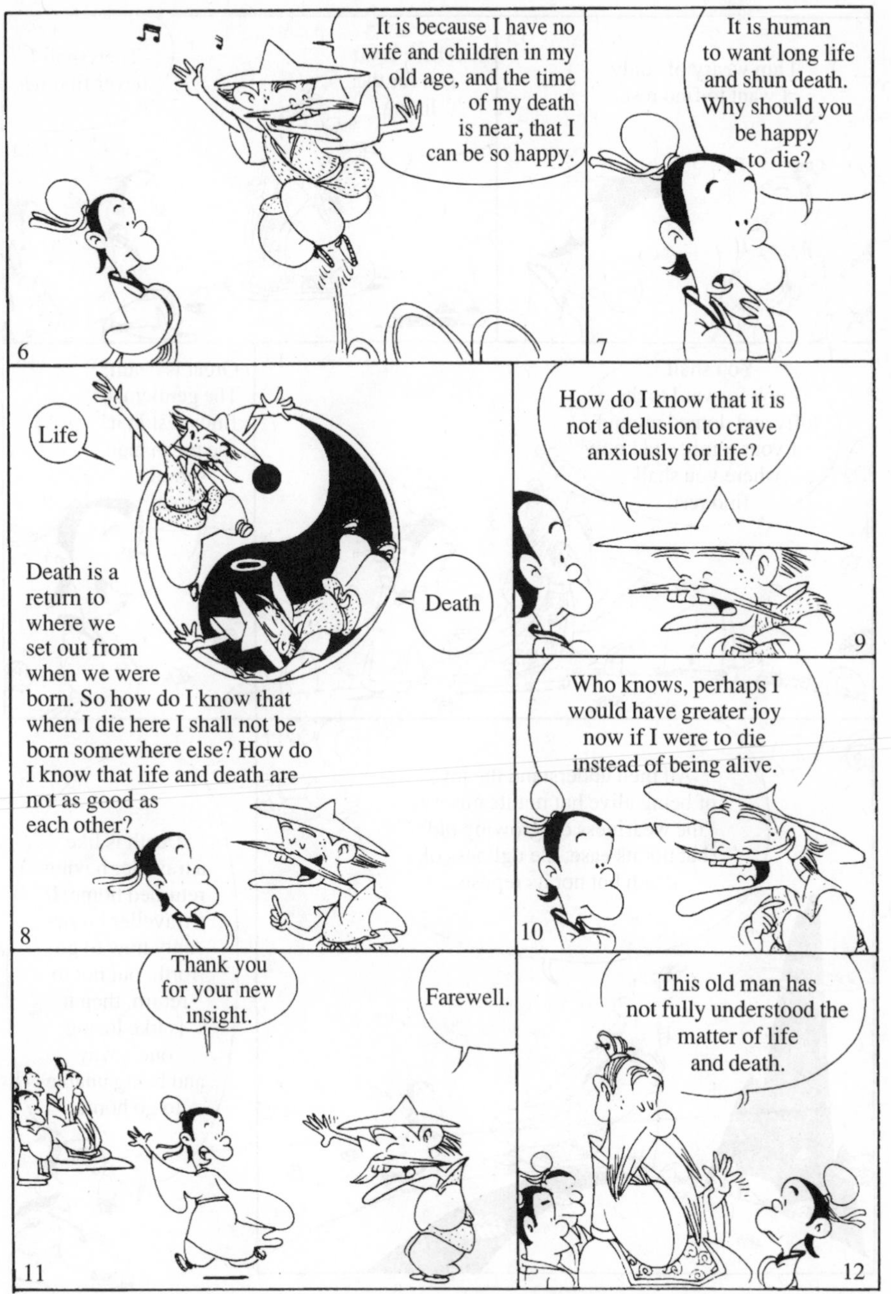
It is because I have no wife and children in my old age, and the time of my death is near, that I can be so happy.
It is human to want long life and shun death. Why should you be happy to die?
Life
Death
Death is a return to where we set out from when we were born. So how do I know that when I die here I shall not be born somewhere else? How do I know that life and death are not as good as each other?
How do I know that it is not a delusion to crave anxiously for life?
Who knows, perhaps I would have greater joy now if I were to die instead of being alive.
Thank you for your new insight.
Farewell.
This old man has not fully understood the matter of life and death.

13
I am weary of study. I want to find rest.
There is no rest for the living.
Then shall I never find it?
14
15
You shall. Look forward to the lofty and domed mound of your tomb, and know where you shall find rest.
16
Great is death! The gentleman finds rest in it, the mean man submits to it!
17
All men understand the joy of being alive but not its misery, the weariness of growing old but not its ease, the ugliness of death but not its repose.
Death is like a traveller having returned home. If a traveller knows only how to go forth, but not to return, then it is like losing one's way and being unable to go home.

Will the sky fall down?
There was a man from the kingdom of Qi who worried every day that the heaven and earth might fall down.
1
z
2
Gosh! Has the sky fallen down?
3
It's really frightening. Looks like the sky is about to fall!
4
Heaven is nothing but the accumulated air; there is no place where there is not air. You are inside heaven all the time; why should you worry about it falling down?
5
If heaven really is accumulated air, shouldn't the sun, moon and stars fall down?
6

7
The sun, moon, and stars are air which shines inside the accumulated air. Even if they fall down, they couldn't hit or harm anyone.
8
What about the earth giving way?
!
The earth is nothing but accumulated soil, filling the void in all four directions. There is no place where there is not soil. You walk and stand on the earth all day; why should you worry about it giving way?
9
Ah, now I have nothing to worry about.
10
11
When Chang Luzi heard this, he said smiling: Since heaven and earth are accumulations of air and soil, how can we say that they will not perish? Heaven and earth are one tiny thing within the void, the largest among things that exist. It is no doubt true that it will be long before they reach their term and come to an end, and it is no easy matter to predict when this will happen. To worry about them perishing is indeed wide of the mark; but to say they will never perish is also open to objection.
The living do not know what it is like to be dead, the dead do not know what it is like to be alive. Coming, we do not know those who went before; going, we shall not know those who come after. Why should we care about whether heaven and earth will perish or not?

The Yellow Emperor

Lie Zi rides the wind
1
Lie Zi had Old Shang as teacher, and Bo Gaozi as his friend.
2
When he had nothing more to learn from either of them, he came home riding the wind.
3
Yin Sheng heard of his abilities and was anxious to learn from him. He kept begging Lie Zi to reveal his secrets, but was turned down each time.
4
Teach me! Teach me! Tell it to me quickly!
5
Teach me how to ride the wind.
6
Damn it! If you don't want to tell me, so be it.
7
What's so great about riding the wind?

A few months later, Yin Sheng came back.
Why do you keep coming and going?
8
I felt some resentment towards you after being rebuffed, but now it is all gone.
9
Let me tell you what I learned from my own master.
10
Three years after I began to serve my master,
My mind no longer dared to think of right and wrong, my mouth no longer dared to speak of gain and loss.
11
It was only then that I got as much as a glance from the master.
12
13
After five years, my mind was again thinking of right and wrong, my mouth was again speaking of gain and loss; and for the first time my master's face relaxed in a smile.
14
After seven years, I thought of whatever came into my mind without any longer distinguishing between right and wrong, said whatever came into my mouth without any longer distinguishing between gain and loss; and for the first time the master pulled me over to sit with him on the same mat.

15
After nine years, I thought of whatever came into my mind and said whatever came into my mind without thinking of right and wrong.
16
Only then, when I had come to the end of everything inside me and outside me, my eyes became like my ears, my ears like my nose, my nose like my mouth; everything was the same.
Sight
Hearing
Smell
17
My mind in unity with everything and my body relaxed,
18
Bones and flesh dissolved into nothingness,
19
I did not notice what my body leaned against and what my feet trod, I drifted with the wind East or West, and never knew whether it was the wind that rode me or I that rode the wind.
20
Now you come to be my disciple, and before even a year has passed, you are indignant and resentful time and again. The air will refuse your slip of a body, the earth will refuse to carry one joint of your finger; can you hope to tread the void and ride the wind?
When the mind is still and no longer thinks of right and wrong, gain and loss, then that mind is the universal mind. It can be said to be inseparable from nature and is also the mountain as well as the ocean. Why can't it be the wind then?

The shaman meets his match
1
A shaman named Ji Xian came from Qi to settle in Zheng state. He could tell whether a man would survive or perish, be lucky or unlucky, die young or live out his span. He would predict the date to the year, the month, the week and the day. The people of Zheng fled when they saw him.
2
Master, I used to think that your Way was peerless, but there is another that goes still farther.
3
I have taught you all that shows on the surface, but you have not exhausted the substance. When you thus match yourself against the world, you are bound to be exposed. That is how you let the man succeed in reading your face.
Try bringing him here, and let him take a look at me.
Yes.
4
My master requests that you read his face for him.
Okay.
5
Alas! Your master is done for. There is no more vitality in him. He cannot last ten days. I saw a strange thing; I saw damp ash in him.

Hee! Hee!
Gosh! Master!
6
Master, please don't die. Ji Xian says your vitality is almost depleted.
7
I have just shown him the configuration of my earth. My breathing, like the life in a growing shoot, did not vibrate yet did not cease. He must have seen me as I am when I check the incipient motions of the virtue within me. Try bringing him again.
8
Please read my master's face again.
9
It is lucky that your master happened to meet me. He will recover. I can see him checking the power in him.
10
I have just shown him my soil fertilized by heaven. Nothing had entered my mind, either as name or as reality. But the incipient breath was coming up from my heels. This is what made him think I was checking the powers in me. He must have seen me as I am when the goodness in me is incipient. Bring him again.
11
Your master has not fasted, so I have nothing to go by. I cannot succeed in reading his face. Try when he has fasted. I will read his face again.
12

13
I have just shown him the absolute emptiness in which there is no foreboding of anything. He must have seen me as I am when I even out the incipient motions of my breath. Whirlpools, still waters, currents, all hollow out deep pools; of the nine kinds of deep pool I have shown him three.
Bring him again.
Yes.
14
15
Wow!
It's scary. He has unlimited power to change himself.
Go after him.
16
17
He has fled. I could not catch up with him.
18

19
I have just shown him myself before we first came out of our Ancestor. With him I dissolved, and drifted in and out of things. Unknowing who and what we were. To him, it seemed we had floundered, it seemed that the waves had swept us away. That is why he fled.
To think I have really not learned anything about the Way...
20
Lie Zi went home and for three years he did not leave his house. He cooked meals for his wife, served food to the pigs as though they were human, and treated all things equally as his kin.
21
From the carved jade he returned to the unhewn block, Till his single shape stood forth, detached from all things. He was free of all tangles, Once and for all, to the end of his life.
To live without limitations of any kind is the highest state of existence.
22

Lie Zi's burden
Lie Zi was on his way to Qi, but turned back halfway. On the road, he met Bohun Wuren.
Why did you turn back in mid-journey?
1
2
I was alarmed by something.
What was it?
I ate at ten inns, and at five they served me first.
I will serve you first.
!
3
4
If that is all, why should you be alarmed?
5
When one has an air of being lofty, it gets him into worldly entanglements.
6
Even an innkeeper with so little to gain from me values me so highly as a customer. What if the Prince of Qi wants to appoint me to some office?
An excellent way to look at it. But even if you stay, other men will lay responsibilities on you.
Yes.
7

Not long afterwards, Bohun Wuren decided to pay Lie Zi a visit.
8
Lie Zi's porch was full of the shoes of visitors.
9
Lie Zi, someone wants to see you.
10
11
Now that you have come, master, aren't you even going to give me your counsel?
12
Enough! I have already told you that others would lay responsibilities on you. It is not that you are capable of allowing them to do so; you are incapable of preventing them. What use is it to you to have this effect on people, which is incompatible with your own peace? If you insist on making an effect, it will unsteady your basic self, and to no purpose.
What you say is true.
To make a display of oneself will attract the attention of others. This is folly rather than wisdom.

Beauty and ugliness

King Mu of Zhou

King Mu's journey of the spirit

7
The king thus built him a magnificent edifice called the Tower in the Middle Sky and his treasury was depleted when the work was completed.
Let me take you to a truly exceptional place that you can feast your eyes on.
Good!
8
9
Wow! I am really flying.
10
It's so beautiful. This must be paradise.
11
Ah, only this can be called the finest palace.

12
Take a look here.
13
I'm scared!
14
Wah!
This place is like hell. Please take me home.
15
16
I beg you, take me home.
17
Please take me home.
You have been sitting here and did not move at all.
18
I didn't move at all? But I'm certain I visit-ed paradise.
19
Your Majesty has been with me on a journey of the spirit. Why should your body have moved? Why should the place you visited be different from your own palace?

20
Your Majesty feels at home with the permanent, is suspicious of the sudden and temporary.
21
But can one always measure how far and how fast a scene may alter and turn into something else?
I see...
22
The king was delighted. He ceased to care for state affairs, took no pleasure in his concubines, and spent his time travelling long journeys.
23
He travelled to the distant Kunlun mountains to look at the Yellow Emperor's palace and also visited the Western Queen Mother.
24
Alas! I, who am king, have neglected virtue for pleasure. Will not future generations look back and chastise me for my errors?
How can we call King Mu a divine man? He was able to enjoy his lifetime to the full, but still he died when his hundred years was up. The world supposed that he had "risen into the sky".

Lao Cheng Zi learns the secret and sublime
I have been here for three years, and you taught me nothing. Perhaps I am not fit to receive your instruction, in which case I had better leave.
Lao Cheng Zi studied magic under Yin Wen, who told him nothing for three years.
Let me say something first...
1
2
Formerly, as Lao Zi was setting out for the West, he looked back and told me:
The breath of all that lives, the appearance of all that has shape, is illusion.
3
What is begun by the creative process, and changed by Yin and Yang, is said to be born and to die.
4
It is when you realise that the illusions and transformations of magic are no different from birth and death that it becomes worthwhile to study magic. You and I are also illusion; what is there to study?
5
Lao Cheng Zi went home to ponder over what Yin Wen told him.
6
After three months of meditation he was able to appear and disappear at will.

He could change the seasons and call up thunder and lightning in winter.
7
8
He could create ice in summer.
9
He could make running things fly...
10
...and flying things run.
11
He never disclosed his magical arts all his life, so that no one handed them down to later generations.
As for those sages who had the art of transforming the empire, their Way was employed in secret. Who has fathomed them?

Lie Zi on dreams

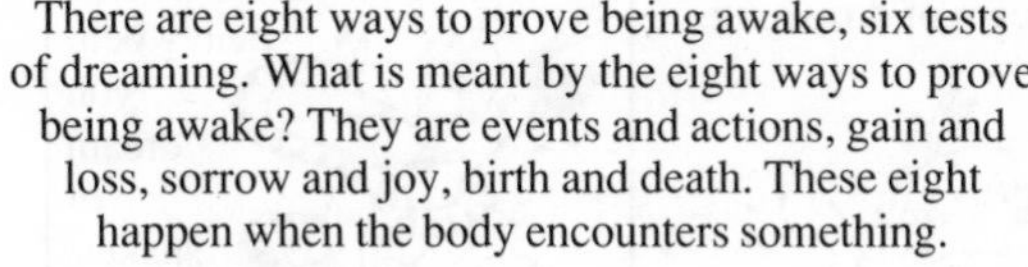

There are eight ways to prove being awake, six tests of dreaming. What is meant by the eight ways to prove being awake? They are events and actions, gain and loss, sorrow and joy, birth and death. These eight happen when the body encounters something.

1

2

What is meant by the six tests? There are normal dreams, and dreams due to alarm, thinking, memory, rejoicing and fear. These six happen when the spirit connects with something. Those who do not recognize where the changes excited in them come from are perplexed about the reason when an event arrives. Those who do recognize where they come from do know the reason; and if you know the reason, nothing will startle you.

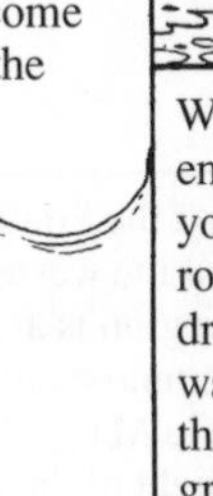

When the Yin energy is strong, you are frightened by dreams of walking through surging waters.

3

When the Yang energy is strong, you are roasted by dreams of walking through great fires.

4

When the Yin and Yang are both strong, you dream of killing or violence.

5

When you starve, you dream of begging for food.

6

When you suffer from giddiness, you dream of floating in the air.

7

8
When you suffer from a sinking, congested feeling, you dream of drowning.
9
When you go to sleep lying on your thick and heavy belt, you dream of snakes.
10
One who is depressed will dream of drinking wine.
11
And after weeping, you will dream of singing and dancing.
12
What we imagine or think about during the day, at night we will dream about. This is due to the interplay of the mind and the body.
13
Z
The True Men of old acted without any sense of self and therefore never dreamed in their sleep.
14
At the South corner of the western region is a country called Gu Mang. The light of the sun and the moon does not shine there, so there is no distinction between day and night. Its people do not eat but sleep most of the time.
Z Z
Z Z
Z Z

15
They think that what they do in dream is real, and what they see waking is unreal.
Z
Z
Z
Z
16
Then there is this place called the Middle Kingdom (China). The Yin and Yang are truly proportioned there, so there is alternation of cold and heat. Darkness and light are rightly divided there, so there is alternation of day and night.
17
They wake and sleep in alternation; and they think that what they do waking is real, and what they see in dreams is unreal.
Z
Z
18
In a country called Fu Le, it is always hot. The people eat anything that does not need cooking. They are always awake and never sleep. By nature they are hard and fierce. The strong oppress the weak.
19
20
I do not know what it means to dream. Food is the only reality.
21
To dream and to be awake - which is real and which is unreal? It is something beyond the ordinary mortal's comprehension.
Life is like a dream. In the interplay of reality and illusion, how can you be sure that you are now not dreaming and that events as seen during a state of dream may be closer to the truth?
Z
Z

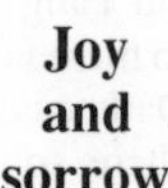

Joy and sorrow

1
Mr Yin of Zhou ran a huge estate. The underlings who hurried to serve him never rested from dawn to dusk.

2
Get up and work, lazybones!
!

3
There was an old servant with little strength in his muscles, whom he drove all the harder.

By day the servant went to work groaning, at night he slept soundly dulled by fatigue.
4

5

Every evening he dreamed that he was lord of the state. He have himself up to whatever pleased him and his joy knew no bounds.

6

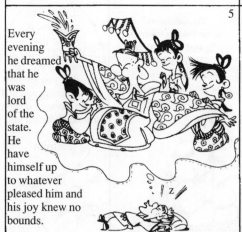

Man's term is a hundred years, divided between day and night. By day I am a servant, and my life is bitter indeed; but at night I become a prince, and my joy is incomparable. Why should I complain?

7
8
Gosh! Another nightmare!
Vexed by worldly affairs, when Mr Yin slept, he dreamed he was a bonded worker.
9
With status and wealth, you think you are above other men. Dreaming at night that you are a slave, reverting from ease to toil, is fortune righting itself.
10
Can you reasonably expect to have it both ways, dreaming as well as awake?
After hearing his friend's advice, Mr Yin eased his demands on the servants.
Don't do such heavy work. Take a rest.
11
12
He also reduced the responsibilities which worried him. As a result, there was harmony in his household and his ailment took a turn for the better.
Whatever bothers the mind is carried over into the dreaming state. When there is peace of mind during one's waking hours, there will be peace of mind as well during sleep.

Dream
or reality?
1
There was a man of Zheng who went to gather firewood in the woods, and came upon a frightened deer. He stood in its way, struck it and killed it.
!
2
Fearing that someone would see the deer, he concealed its body.
3
But he later forgot where he hid the deer, and concluded that he must have been dreaming. He came down the road mumbling to himself.
Is it a dream or reality?
!
4
I'll look for the deer based on what he said.
5
Oh, there really is a deer hidden here.
6
Just now a woodcutter dreamed he had caught a deer, but did not know where he kept it. Now I have found it. His dream was a true one.
7
Isn't it rather that you dreamed the woodcutter catch the deer? Why should there be any woodcutter? Since you have really got the deer, isn't it your dream which was true?

8
All I know is that I have got it. What do I care which of us was dreaming?
That's true
9
The man who killed the deer dreamed of where he hid it.
10
He also dreamed that a man had taken his deer.
z z
11
Is it a dream?
Or is it real?
12
Let me see whether I can find the deer based on what I dreamed.
13
So it is you who stole my deer.
But I found it.
14
The case went to court.
15
At first the deer was yours, and yet you said it was a dream. Then you dreamed about the deer, and said it was reality. Now all I know is that here we have the deer. I suggest you divide it between the two of you.
The woodcutter's gain, forgetfulness, and dream of the deer can be likened to gain and loss in everyday life. It is as illusory as a dream.

Loss of memory
In the state of Song there was a person named Hua Zi who lost his memory at middle age. When out in the streets he would forget to return home. Today he would not remember yesterday, tomorrow he would not remember today.
?
?
1
What is this place?
It's your home!
2
May I know your name?
I'm your wife!
3
If there is anyone who can help him regain his memory, I will reward him.
4
A Confucian gentleman approached her.
Let me try to cure him.
Let me spend seven days with him. I shall try to reform his mind and change his thoughts.
Thank you!
6
No one knew what methods the Confucian used, but he cured Hua Zi of his loss of memory.
7
When Hua Zi woke up he was very angry. He chased away his wife.
Get lost!
8

He scolded and beat his son for no reason.
Fool!
9
10
Wielding a chopper, he sent the Confucian fleeing for his life.
Don't get agitated. You may kill someone.
Let go of me.
11
13
Formerly, when I forget, I was carefree. I did not notice whether heaven and earth existed or not. Now suddenly I remember, and all the disasters and recoveries, gains and losses, joys and sorrows, loves or hates of twenty or thirty years past resurface in a thousand tangled threads.
Hee!
12
Why have you become so violent after recovering from your loss of memory?
14
I fear that all the things still to come will confound my heart just as much. Shall I never again find a moment of forgetfulness?
Concepts of gain and loss, joy and sorrow, good and bad, are all man-made. If one wants to live a life of freedom, then one must not be caught in such states of duality.

Who is normal?
Mr Pang of Qin state had a son who suffered from an abnormality. When the son saw white he thought it was black and his sense of smell was distorted.
1
Black.
2
Smelly!
3
Fragrant!
4
The Confucians in Lu state are knowledgeable. Perhaps they can help you.
I'll take my son there.
5
The father set out for Lu, but while passing through the state of Chen, he met Lao Zi.
How do you know that your son is abnormal? Nowadays everyone in the world is deluded about right and wrong, and confused about benefit and harm. Because so many people share this sickness, no one perceives that it is a sickness.
6
Supposing the minds of everyone in the world were like your son's, then on the contrary it is you who would be abnormal.
7
Good and evil, black and white are all subjected to human definition. They have no independent objective standards. If everyone says white is black, then wouldn't it be you who believe otherwise who is muddle-headed?

Tricks of the mind
1
There was a man who was born in Yan state but grew up in Chu, and in his old age returned to his native place. While he was passing through the state of Qin his companion played a joke on him.
2
This is the capital of Yan.
!
He composed himself and looked solemn.
3
This is the shrine of your area.
He breathed a deep sigh.
4
His tears welled up.
This is your ancestral home.
5
Take a look there...
Sob!
6
This is your father's tomb.

!
Oh!
Ha! Ha! Ha! This is most amusing!
I was teasing you. You are still only in Qin.
!
Hee! Hee!
Prankster!
When he finally reached Yan and really saw the capital and the shrine in his area, really saw his ancestral home and his father's tomb...
…he did not feel it so deeply.
Sorrow is merely a state of mind and may not be warranted by the circumstances. Hence whether or not you feel sad over something is all in the mind.

Confucius

Who is a sage?
The chief minister of the state of Song visited Confucius.
Are you a sage?
How can I claim to be a sage? I am merely a man who has studied widely and remembered much.
1
2
Were the Three Kings sages?
3
The Three Kings were good at employing wisdom and courage; whether they were sages I do not know.
4
Were the Five Emperors sages?
5
The Five Emperors were good at employing morality; whether they were sages I do not know.

6
Were the Three Highnesses sages?
7
The Three Highnesses were good at adapting themselves to the times; whether they were sages I do not know.
Then who do you think is a sage?
8
Among the people of the Western regions there is a sage. He does not govern, yet there is no disorder; does not speak, yet is trusted spontaneously; does not reform, yet his influence prevails spontaneously.
9
He is so great that none of his people can give a name to him. I suspect that he is a sage, but I do not know whether he truly is or not.
Confucius is deceiving me!
10
A sage is usually someone recognized as such by others. When someone claims to be a sage serving society and the nation, he is actually seeking self-benefit.

The disciples' shortcomings
Zi Xia asked Confucius:
What sort of man is Yan Hui?
For kindness, he is a better man than I am.
1
2
What about Zi Kong?
For eloquence, he is a better man than I am.
3
What about Zi Lu?
For courage, he is a better man than I am.
4
Zi Zhang?
5
6
For dignity, he is a better a man than I am.
Then why do these four serve you ?
Don't get agitated. Sit calmly and I'll tell you.
7

8
Yan Hui can be kind, but cannot check the impulse when it will do no good.
9
Zi Kong can be eloquent, but cannot hold his tongue.
10
Zi Lu can be brave but cannot be cautious.
11
Zi Zhang can be digni-fied, but cannot unbend in company.
12
Even if I could have the virtues of the four men all together, I should be unwilling to exchange them for my own. This is why they serve me without misgivings.
A teacher maintains his position among disciples primarily because his vision is greater than theirs. Whatever their virtues, they cannot surpass him in wisdom.

The joy
of travel
Lie Zi, you like to travel. Tell me why you like to travel.
The joy of travel is that the things which amuse you never remain the same. Other men travel to contemplate the sights, I travel to contemplate the way things change.
Is not your travel really the same as other men's? Anything at all that we see, we always see changing. You are amused that other things never remain the same, but do not know that you yourself never remain the same.
You busy yourself with outward travel and do not know how to busy yourself with inward contemplation. By outward travel we seek what we lack in things outside us while by inward contemplation we find sufficiency in ourselves.
The latter is the perfect, the former an imperfect kind of travelling.
After hearing his teacher Hu Zi's words, Lie Zi gave up travelling.
One who travels because he is attracted by outward beauty will either feel elation or disappointment at what he sees. He can never be completely satisfied with his travels.

The Questions of Tang

The things of creation

In the kingdom of the Dragon Lord, the people are ten metres tall.
I am three metres shorter than my peers, and everybody calls me a dwarf.
6
7
East of China, we come to the kingdom of Jiao Yao, where the people are one foot five inches tall.
In the far North East there are the people called Zheng who are nine inches tall.
Does time has the distinction of long and short?
8
9
In the southern ocean there is a kind of turtle which lives long. It grows through a spring of five hundred years and declines through an autumn of five hundred years.
In ancient times there was a great chun tree, whose spring and autumn were eight thousand years each.
10

11
There are insects which are born in the morning and dies by evening.
12
Do things have the distinction of big and small, long and short?
Let me explain.
13
In the northern ocean there is a fish called the kun which is of gargantuan size.
There is a bird there called the peng, with wings like clouds hanging from the sky, and a body big in proportion.
14
Between the shores of the Changjiang, minute insects breed, named jiao ming, which fly in swarms and gather on the eyelashes of mosquitoes without jostling each other, coming to land and leaving without the mosquitoes noticing.

In order to see the insects, the Yellow Emperor and Rong Chengzi meditated and fasted for three months.
15
They then saw that the jiao ming was indeed huge and made a sound as loud as thunder.
16
What is useful, and what is not?
You cannot say for sure.
17
In the countries of Wu and Chu there is a tree called the pomelo. Eating its skin and juice cures fits.
18
But when it is planted north of the Huai river, the fruit it produces is tiny and inedible.
19
I understand now. It is only when things are being compared that the distinctions of long and short, high and low, big and small and manifestation and nothingness come into being. The mind can be free only when it ceases to discriminate and compare.
20
Creation produces myriad forms. Whatever one's form, one should cherish and take good care of it and use it to live well.

Moving the mountain

1
The mountains Tai Xing and Wang Wu were thousands of feet high. They stood originally between Jizhou on the north and Heyang on the south. When Mr Simple of North Mountain was nearly ninety, he was living opposite them. It vexed him that, with the north flank of the mountains blocking the road, it was such a long way round to come and go.
2
Do you agree that we should make every effort to level the mountains, so that there is a clear road straight to the south of Yu and down to the south bank of the Han river?
Agreed.
Yes.
3
You are too weak to reduce even the smallest hillock. What can you do with Tai Xing and Wang Wu? Besides, where will you put the earth and rocks?
4
Throw them in the tail of the Gulf of Zhili north of Yintu.
5
Thus he began his work, with his sons and grandsons helping him.

You are so old already. Even if you work yourself to death you will not be able to level the mountains.
What can you do to earth and stones? Unless you can make one supreme effort to shift them, you will weep at the task.
You are the one who is stupid. Even when I die, I shall have sons and grandsons surviving me.
My descendants will go on perpetuating the family line, but the mountains will get no bigger. Why should there be any difficulty in levelling them?
The mountain spirit came to know about his endeavour. Moved by his sincerity, he commanded the two sons of the guardian deity of the mountain to do the job.
However difficult a task, if you do not set out to accomplish it, how can you know that you cannot do it? With resolve and determination, even mountains can be moved.

Kua Fu chases the sun
1
The deity Kua Fu wanted to bring the sun down to earth so that it would always give its light and there would be no darkness.
2
Stay where you are! Don't try to flee.
3
He pursued the sun for thousands of miles.
4
Gosh! I'm dying of thirst.
5
He drank from the Yellow River and the Wei river.

6
His thirst was not quenched and he ran north intending to drink the Great Marsh.
7
Whew!
8
But he died of thirst on the way and the ground shook as his body fell.
Hee! Hee!
The days and the years passed...
9
10
The sun and the elements disintegrated his body.
11
Soon, his body became the nourishment for other living things which grew on it.
One must know one's own strength and limitation and not over-exert oneself. One who tries to defy nature will suffer the consequences.

Traditions and customs
1
East of Yue is the country of Chemu. When a first son is born they cut him up and eat him. They say this will make the mother more fertile.
2
When a grandfather dies, they carry off the grandmother on their backs and abandon her. They say this is because "it is not right to live with the wife of a ghost".
3
West of Qin is the country of Yiqu. When a parent or kinsman dies, they would have failed in their duty as filial sons unless they collect a pile of firewood and burn him on it. When the smoke goes up they say he has risen to the sky.
Traditions and customs are set by people. Therefore what people regard as "truth" tends to be a subjective matter. What is considered right would be seen as wrong at a different time and under different circumstances.

Spirit of the lute
1
When Hu Ba played the lute, the birds danced and fishes bounded.
Wen of Zheng heard this story, and left his family to be an apprentice to music master Xiang.
2
Master, please teach me the art of lute-playing.
Let's see if you have the aptitude.
3
Sigh!
4
He would lay his fingers on the strings to tune them but for three years, he could not even complete playing a single tune.
5
You had better leave.
Yes.

6
It is not the strings that I cannot tune, nor the piece that I cannot finish. What I have in mind is not in the strings, what I am aiming at is not in the notes.
7
Unless I grasp it inwardly in my heart, it will not answer from the instrument outside me. That is why I dare not put out my hand to pluck the strings.
8
Wen left his master for a period of time, then made his way back.
9
How are you getting on with the lute?
I have got it. Let me show you.
10

11
!
12
13
It was spring at this time and he touched the autumn string and called up the note of the eighth month. A cool wind came suddenly and fruits ripened on the bushes and trees.
14
When autumn came he touched the spring string and aroused the note of the second month. A warm breeze whirled gently, and the bushes and trees burst into flower.
During the summer he touched the winter string and called up the note of the eleventh month. Frost and snow fell together and the rivers and lakes abruptly froze.
15

16
When winter came he touched the summer string and aroused the note of the fifth month. The sunlight burned fiercely and the hard ice melted at once.
17
Well, what do you say?
Your playing is sublime!
18
Even the music master Guang performing the qing jiao music and Shou Yan blowing the pitch-tubes had nothing to add to this. Guang's performance of the qing jiao caused a drought which lasted three years. Shou Yan, by blowing the pitch-tubes, warmed the climate of a country in the far north. They would have to put their lutes under their arms, take their pipes in their hands, and follow behind you.
A person of calibre does not concern himself with external passing events, but with what goes on in his mind. It is pure awareness that enables him to penetrate into the heart of things.

Singing with heart and soul
1
Xue Tan studied singing under Qin Qing. Before he had fathomed Qin Qing's art he thought he had no more to learn, so he took his leave.
2
Master, I think I have learned enough. I would like to leave.
Very well.
3
Let me sing you a song to bid you farewell.
Thank you.
4
Qin Qing's song had an air of melancholy. The sound shook the trees in the forest.
5

6
Even the drifting clouds in the sky above came to a standstill.
8
9
Then Xue Tan apologized and asked to be taken back, and for the rest of his life never dared to speak of going home.

10
His master told him: Once upon a time in Han lived a woman named Han Er. She ran out of provisions while travelling east to Qi.
11
She entered the capital through the Concord Gate, and traded her songs for a meal.
12
When she left, the lingering notes curled round the beams of the gate and did not die away for three days. The bystanders thought that she was still there.
13
She passed an inn and the innkeeper insulted her.
14
She therefore wailed mournfully in long-drawn-out notes.
15
All the people in the quarter, young and old, looked at each other sadly with the tears rolling down their faces.

16
They were so depressed that they could not eat for three days.
17
They hurried after her and brought her back.
18
19
20
She sang them a ballad and everyone, young and old, could not help dancing with joy, forgetting that they had been sad just before. Afterwards they sent her away with lavish presents.
21
That is why even today the people of Concord Gate are good singers and funeral wailers, taking as their example the memory of Han Er's singing.
That which comes from the depths of one's being cannot but have an effect on others. Time cannot diminish its impact.

A friend after one's own heart
1
Bo Ya was an accomplished lute-player, and Zhong Ziqi was a good listener.
2
Bo Ya strummed his lute, with his mind on climbing high mountains.
3
Marvellous! Lofty like Taishan.

4
When Bo Ya's mind was on flowing waters...
Superb! Boundless like the Yellow River and the Changjiang.
5
One day, they were roaming on the north side of Taishan when they were caught in a sudden storm of rain.
6
Overcome by a sense of melancholy, Bo Ya took up his lute and strummed it. First he composed a piece about the persistent rain.
!
7
Like droplets of rain...
8
Like a steady patter...
9
Like a torrent...

10
Bo Ya then improvised the sound of crashing mountains.
Excellent! The sounds of your lute reflect the sounds of the natural surroundings!
11
It is now like the crashing of rocks.
12
How well you listen! What you imagine is just what is in my mind. Is there nowhere for my notes to flee to?
Is that so?
Feelings of the heart are communicated in a non-verbal manner. Although no words are being spoken, there can be tacit understanding on the part of another. A friend after one's own heart is hard to find. If you have got such a friend, what more can be lacking?

The sublime archer
1
During the time of the Warring States, there was a young man named Ji Chang who aspired to be the greatest archer in the land.
2
Fei Wei is the best archery teacher. You can't go wrong if you learn from him.
Ji Chang thus crossed mountains and forded rivers and braved all forms of hardship in order to seek out Fei Wei.
3
4
Fei Wei's skill was exceptional and he could hit a willow leaf with his arrow from a distance of a hundred paces. Of course, he did not teach Ji Chang archery immediately.
5
You must learn not to blink before you can talk about archery.
6
Ji Chang went home and lay down under his wife's loom, with his eye next to the pedal.

7
After two years he did not blink even when the sharp end of an object reached the corner of his eye.
8
Next you must learn how to look. Come and tell me when you can see the small as though it were big, the faint as though it were distinct.
Yes.
9
Ji Chang hung a flea at his window by a hair from a yak's tail, and watched it from a distance with the sun behind it.
10
Within three months he could see the flea as large as a moth. After a year, it was the size of a pig.
11
At the end of three years it was as big as a buffalo.
12
When he looked at other things in the same way, even a horse seemed as big as a mountain.

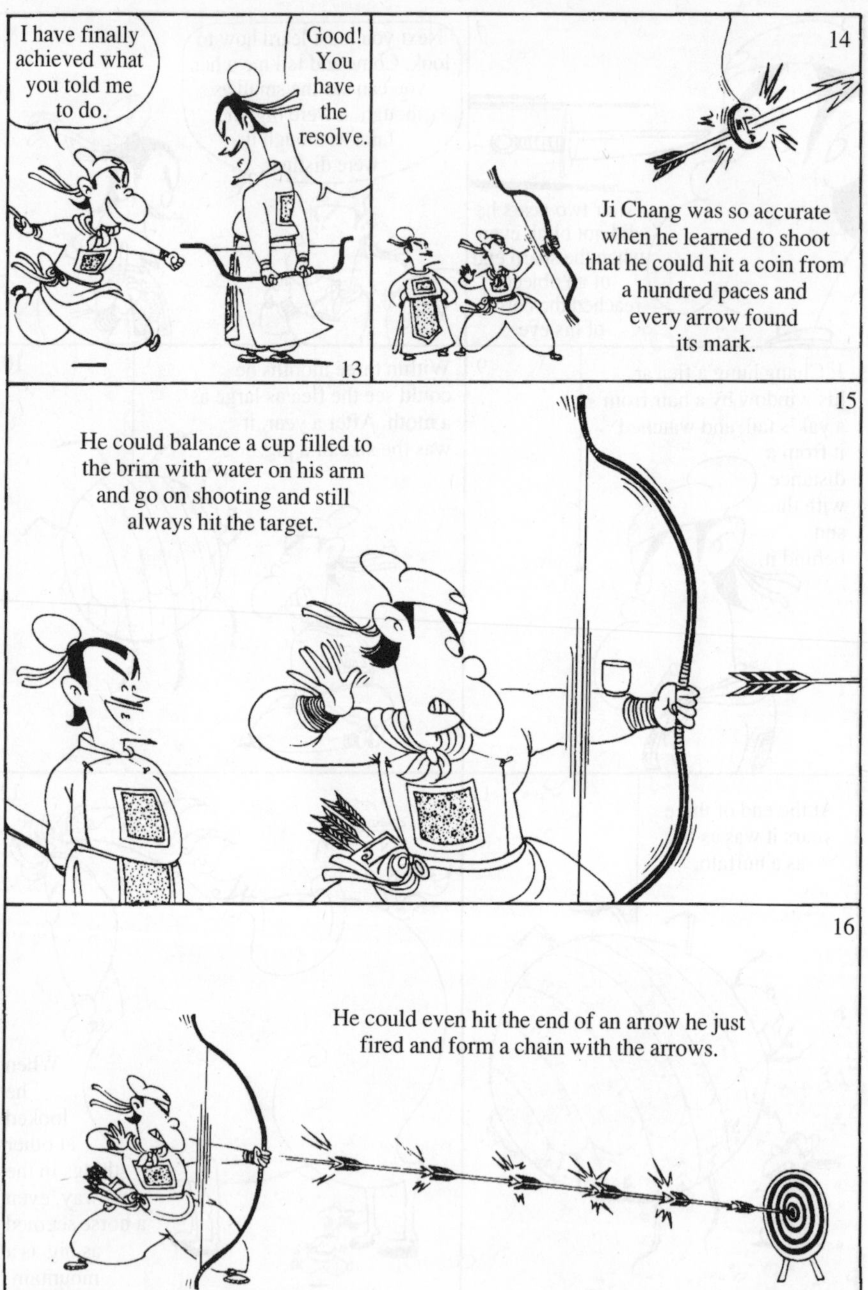
I have finally achieved what you told me to do.
Good! You have the resolve.
13
14
Ji Chang was so accurate when he learned to shoot that he could hit a coin from a hundred paces and every arrow found its mark.
15
He could balance a cup filled to the brim with water on his arm and go on shooting and still always hit the target.
16
He could even hit the end of an arrow he just fired and form a chain with the arrows.

17
When he returned home, his wife was not happy to see him.
You do no work but spend all your time looking for things to shoot. What kind of a husband are you?
18
Ji Chang fired an arrow at his wife and he was so quick that she did not notice it whizz-ing past her and slicing off some of her eyelashes.
19
Ji Chang considered himself the peerless archer.
20
Fei Wei
He judged that only one man was a match for himself.
21
One day, he saw Fei Wei in the moor and decided to challenge him to a duel.
22
Their arrow-heads collided in mid-air and dropped to the ground.
!

23
Whatever arrows Ji Chang fired was easily intercepted by Fei Wei.
24
Aiyah! I have run out of arrows!
25
Meet your doom!
26
Fei Wei caught the arrow-head in his teeth!
27
Wow!
28
Thereupon the two men threw aside their bows weeping, embraced each other and vowed to become like father and son. They drew blood from their arms and took an oath never to reveal their arts to other men.

29
I have imparted to you everything I know about archery. If you want the supreme skill, you will have to learn from my master Gan Ying.
30
Compared to his skill, ours is like child's play. He lives on a distant mountain.
31
Ji Chang set off at once to look for the master.
32
After untold hardships, he finally reached Gan Ying's abode.
33
Are you master Gan Ying?
That is so.

34
Would you say I am a great archer?
35
How's that?
Not bad.
36
But you still need an arrow to hit the bird. That is not the supreme skill.
37
Have you learned how to shoot without an arrow?
38
What? Can one shoot without an arrow?
39
Follow me.

40
Wah!
41
Now show me your archery skill.
Oh no, I can't do it here.
42
Let me show you the true art of archery.
Where's your bow and arrow?
43
As long as you need a bow and arrow, you will never grasp the sublime art of archery.
44
Come down!
!
45
The highest archery does not require a bow and arrow.

46
Ji Chang remained under Gan Ying's tutelage for nine years. As to what he learned from Gan Ying, no one knew.
47
After ten years, Ji Chang left the mountain. He underwent a complete transformation and the brashness in him had completely disappeared.
48
Ji Chang, I can see that you are now a peerless archer. Even if I were your underling I would feel unworthy of you.
Not at all.

49
The people wanted to watch him display his skill, but he made no move. He did not keep a bow, let alone an arrow.
50
Ji Chang, show us what you are capable of!
Why don't you shoot?
51
Movement without motion, speaking without sound, shooting without arrow, why should I shoot?
The supreme archer has no sense of self and other, bow and arrow. He is complete in himself.
52
Ji Chang thus lived in peace for the next forty years. It was said that on the roof of his home was an invisible set of bow and arrow which even the birds dared not approach.

The art of the charioteer
Zao Fu wanted to learn charioteering from Tai Dou and served him for three years. Though he behaved with the utmost humility, Tai Dou told him nothing.
1
2
The son of a good bow-maker must begin by making baskets.
3
The son of a good blacksmith must begin by making chisels.
Yes.
Tai Dou thus put a row of wooden stumps on the ground and told Zao Fu to watch him run. "First watch me run. You will not be able to hold six bridles and drive six horses until you can run like me."
4
5
Tai Dou ran forwards and backwards stepping from one to the next without stumbling. Zao Fu practised it and could do it perfectly in three days.

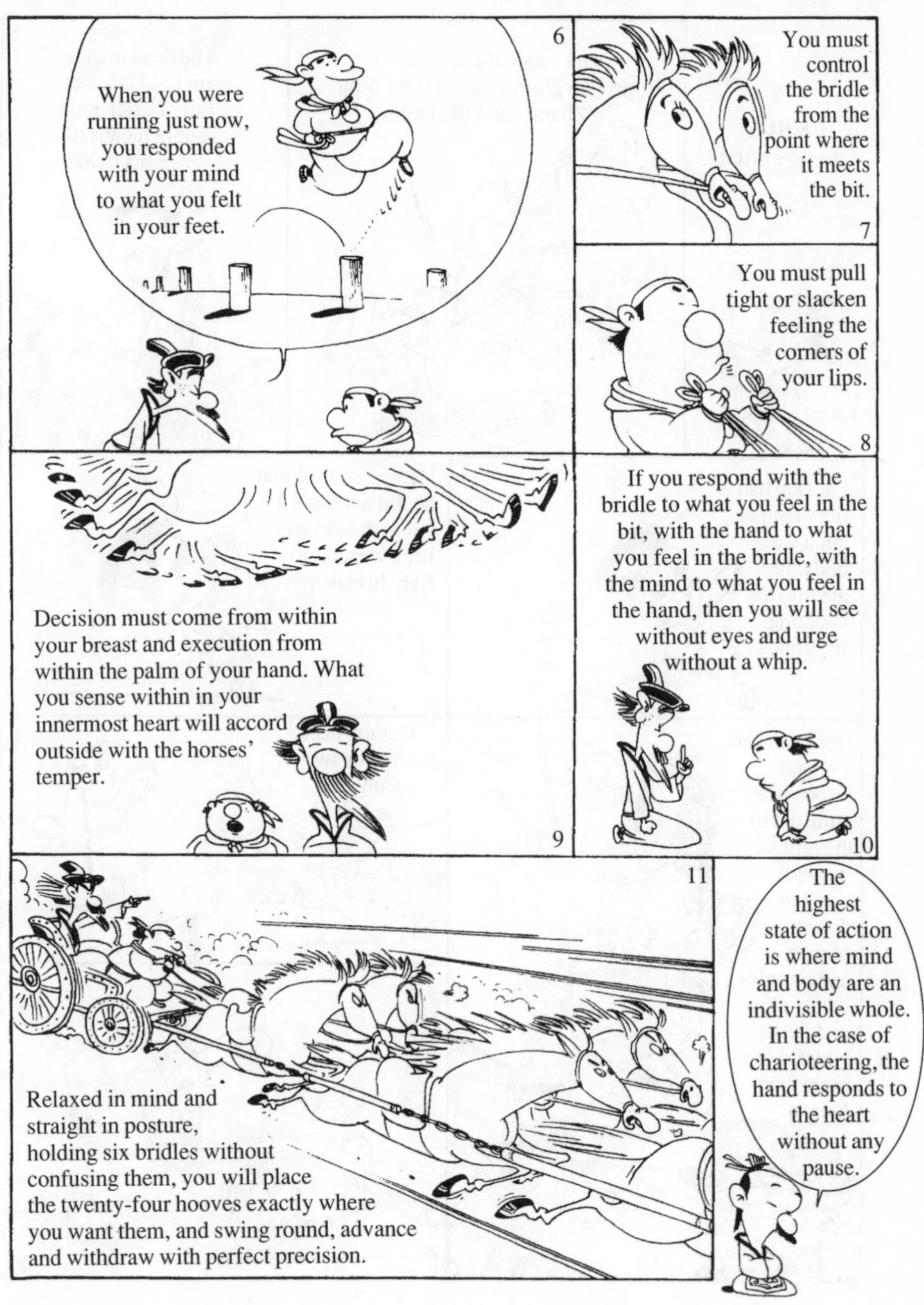
6
When you were running just now, you responded with your mind to what you felt in your feet.
You must control the bridle from the point where it meets the bit.
7
You must pull tight or slacken feeling the corners of your lips.
8
Decision must come from within your breast and execution from within the palm of your hand. What you sense within in your innermost heart will accord outside with the horses' temper.
9
If you respond with the bridle to what you feel in the bit, with the hand to what you feel in the bridle, with the mind to what you feel in the hand, then you will see without eyes and urge without a whip.
10
11
Relaxed in mind and straight in posture, holding six bridles without confusing them, you will place the twenty-four hooves exactly where you want them, and swing round, advance and withdraw with perfect precision.
The highest state of action is where mind and body are an indivisible whole. In the case of charioteering, the hand responds to the heart without any pause.

A son's vengeance
1
Hei Luan of Liang had a private grudge against Qiu Bing Zhang and killed him.
2
The dead man's son Lai Dan was full of grief and sought means to avenge his father.
3
Lai Dan had a fiery temper but a weak body; he ate his rice counting the grains.
4
He was so frail that he did not have the strength to even lift a weapon to fight his enemy.
5
Hei Luan had a savage disposition quite out of the ordinary, strength equal to dozens of men, and muscles, bones, skin and flesh which were more than human.
Heh!
6
Cut my neck with your sword. Come on, be quick!
7

8
That bum Lai Dan wants to take revenge on me. I am ready for him anytime!
Wow!
9
There is no hope. It seems there is no way I can kill Hei Luan to avenge my father.
10
I heard that the grandfather of Kong Zhou of Wei won the treasured swords of the Yin emperors. A single small boy with one of these swords at his side could drive back a whole army. Why not ask him for help?
11
So Lai Dan went to Wei and met Kong Zhou. Before making his request, he addressed Kong Zhou with the politeness of an underling, and offered him his wife and children as slaves.
I have three swords, but none of them can kill anyone.
12
The first is called Container of Light. Look for it and it is invisible, swing it and you cannot tell it is there. When it hits something there is no cut whatever; it passes right through without the victim noticing.
13
The second is called the Receiver of Shadows. In the twilight just before dawn, if you scrutinize it with your back to the sun, there is a faint resemblance of something there, but no one can recognize its shape. When it hits something there is a hissing sound, and it passes right through without hurting the victim.

The third is called Tempered by Night. By day you see its shadow but not its glitter, by night its glitter but not its shape. When it strikes something, it passes through with a tearing sound, and the wound closes as soon as it has passed. The victim feels pain but there is no stain on the blade.
14
These three treasures have been handed down through thirteen generations without being put to use. I have kept them in their cases and never broken the seals.
15
Which of the swords would you like?
I want the third one.
16
Kong Zhou fasted with him for seven days and on the twilight of the seventh day, presented the sword to Lai Dan.
17
18
So Lai Dan went looking for Hei Luan with the sword by his side.
19
Picking a time when Hei Luan was lying drunk under his window, he wreaked his vengeance.
z
z
Here's my chance.
20

21
Hei Luan, I'm going to kill you.
He slashed Hei Luan three times from neck to waist.
Z
Z
22
What have you done to my father?
I will kill you as well.
Wah! What are you doing?
23
24
Why did you wave your hand at me three times in that funny way?
This sword really can't kill anyone.
25
26
Even though I have not actually killed anyone, at least I have fulfilled my wish for revenge.
A sword that could repel a huge army in days past is no longer useful. Similarly, some of the dictums of the people of old may no longer be applicable in today's world.

Endeavour and Destiny

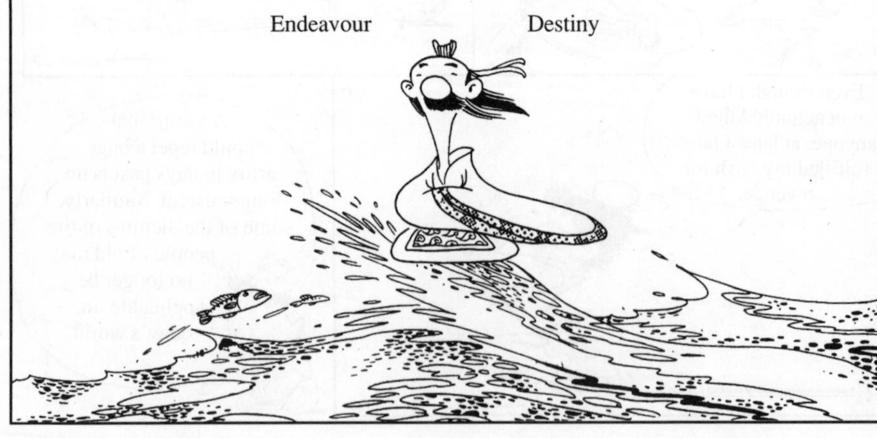

Destiny

1
Yang Bu asked his elder brother Yang Zhu:
Take the case of two men, who are as alike as brothers in age, speech, talents and appearance, yet as unlike as father and son in their time of death, rank, reputation, and the affection given them by others.
I am perplexed by this.
It is all a matter of destiny.
2
3
All that happens without us knowing why is destiny. For the man who trusts destiny, there is no difference between long life and short. For one who trusts his mind, there is nothing which is agreeable or offensive.
Then we may say that there is nothing which he either trusts or distrusts.
He is true, he is genuine. What should he shun or approach, enjoy or grieve over, do or not do?
4
The highest man gives no thought to why he exists and why he acts. He neither changes his feelings and expression because ordinary people are watching, nor fails to change them because ordinary people are not watching. He comes alone and goes alone; what can obstruct him?

Clinging to life and shunning death
Duke Jing of Qi went on an excursion to Ox Mountain.
How beautiful, this city of mine, teeming and thriving!
But some day I will have to die and leave this place forever.
Your servants owe it to your bounty that we are here today. Yet even we do not wish to die, and how much less our master!
Ho! Ho! Ho!
Yan Zi, why are you laughing?
Ha!
My excursion today has been a melancholy one. My two ministers both wept as I did. Why should you alone be laughing?

7
If by merit alone we could hold on to life, your ancestors
Tai Gong and Duke Huan would have lived forever. If by courage we could hold on to life, Duke Zhuang and Duke Ling would have lived forever.
8
If these princes had held on to life, my lord would now be in the ricefields caring about nothing but his work, with no time to think about death. For how does my lord come to be sitting on his throne?
9
Because your ancestors occupied it one after another until it was your turn. And it is ignoble that you should be the only one shedding tears over it.
10
I see an ignoble lord and two sycophantic ministers, and this is the reason why I alone found it amusing.
11
Duke Jing was ashamed of himself. He recovered his spirits and toasted a drink to his ministers.
One should face life and death squarely and live with courage and confidence. To cling to life and fear death is to be like a traveller going astray and being on a journey of no return.

Death is nothing to grieve over

There was a man of Wei named Wu, who did not grieve when his son died.
1

Boss, give me three jin* of wine.
2
3
No one loved his son as much as you did. Why do you not go home and grieve now that he has died?

4
I used to have no son, and when I had no son I did not grieve. Now that he is dead, it is the same as it was before when I had no son. Why should I grieve over him?

Why should one grieve over death? Most people regard those who have seen through death as somewhat abnormal because they do not grieve. But what is one to do? Be depressed and in low spirits because of grief?

* 1 jin = $\frac{1}{2}$ kg

Yang Zhu

1

Yang Zhu is regarded as a Taoist, but his philosophy of life is different from Taoism in many ways.

2

His message is very simple: Life is short, and the only good reasons for living are music, companionship, fine clothes and tasty food. He seems to have held that, since external possessions are replaceable while the body is not, we should never permit the least injury to the body, even the loss of a hair, for the sake of any external benefit, even the throne of the empire.

The emptiness of fame
When Yang Zhu was in Lu, he stayed with Mr Meng.
We are simply the men we are. What use is reputation?
A reputation helps us to get rich.
1
Once rich, why not be done with it?
It helps us to attain high rank.
2
Once we have high rank, why not be done with it?
3
It will help when we are dead.
4
Once dead, what good will it do us?
It will help our descendants.
5
What use will our reputations be to our descendants?
6

7
Caring for reputation vexes the body and withers the heart. But the man who takes advantage of his reputation can prosper his whole clan and benefit his whole district, not to speak of his descendants.
8
But whoever cares for reputation must be honest, and if honest he will be poor. He must be humble, and if humble he will not rise in rank.
9
When Guan Zhong was Chief Minister in Qi, he was lewd when his ruler was lewd, extravagant when his ruler was extravagant. He accorded with his ruler in thought and in speech, and by the practice of his way the state won hegemony. But after his death, the Guan family was still the Guan family.
10
When Tian Heng was Chief Minister in Qi, he behaved unassumingly when his ruler was arrogant and behaved generously when his ruler was grasping. The people all went over to him, and in this way he won possession of the state of Qi, and his descendants have enjoyed it without interruption down to the present day.

So if you really live up to your reputation, you will be poor; if your reputation is pretence, you will be rich.
That's right.
11
Reality has nothing to do with reputation, reputation has nothing to do with reality. Reputation is nothing but pretence.
12
Formerly Yao and Shun claimed they wanted to give up the empire to Xu Yu and Shan Chuan and thus acquired a good reputation for their generosity. In fact they eventually did not do so and kept the empire for themselves. They won a good reputation without losing an empire.
13
14
Bo Yi and Shu Qi, who really gave up the fief of Gu Zhu, did end up losing the state, and dying of starvation on Mount Shou Yang.
15
The difference between the reality and the pretence could not be put more plainly.
In the world, one cannot have it both ways. If he wants to maintain his good reputation, he must not think of pursuing status and wealth. But if he wants status and riches, he must bear in mind that it will be at the expense of his integrity.

Life is short

1

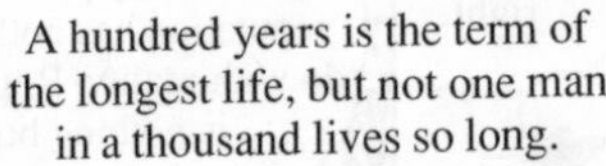

A hundred years is the term of the longest life, but not one man in a thousand lives so long.

2

Should there be one who lives out his span, infancy and senility take nearly half of it.

3

The nights lost in sleep, the days wasted even when we are awake, take nearly half of the rest.

4

Pain and sickness, sorrow and toil, ruin and loss anxiety and fear take nearly half of the rest.

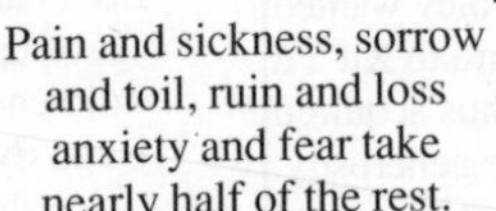

Of the dozen or so years which remain, if we reckon how long we are at ease and content, without the least care, the time can be measured in moments.

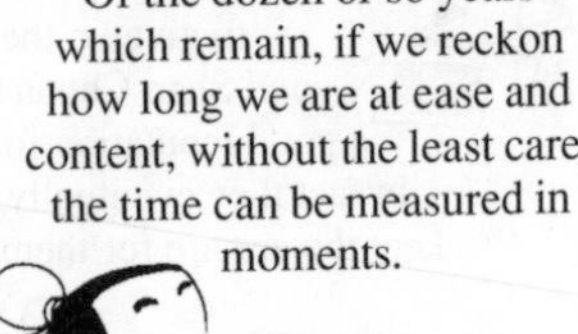

5

6

Then what is a man to live for? Where is he to find happiness?

7

In fine clothes, delicious food, music and beautiful women? But we cannot always have enough good clothes and food to satisfy us, cannot always be dallying with women and listening to music.

Are we to fritter away our life in pursuit of the impermanent?
8
One will then not be able to distinguish good and bad no matter what he hears.
9
One will not be able to appreciate beauty which is right in front of one's eyes.
10
One who cannot even lead a peaceful life, in what way is he better than a criminal or a pariah?
11
In life we are here for a moment and in death we are gone for a moment. Therefore we should pursue our heart's prompting and not restrain our natural inclinations.
12
We should roam as our nature prompts us and not rebel against the tendencies common to all things. In following what is our nature, we are on common ground with all beings.
13
If one does not seek a reputation in life or want a good name after death, then whether one lives long or short does not matter. Just live and enjoy life.

Life and death

It is in life that the myriad things of the world are different;

1

2

In death they are the same. In life, there are clever and foolish, noble and vile; these are the differences. In death there are stench and rot, decay and extinction; in this we are all the same.

3

However, whether we are clever or foolish, noble or vile, is not our own doing,

4

And neither are stench and rot, decay and extinction.

5

Hence we do not bring about our own life or death, cleverness or foolishness, nobility or vileness. However, the myriad things all equally live and die, are equally clever and foolish, noble and vile.

6
Some in ten years, some in a hundred, we all die.
7
Saints and sages die, the wicked and foolish die. In life they were Yao and Shun, in death they were rotten bones.
8
In life they were Jie and Zhou, in death they were rotten bones.
9
Rotten bones are all the same, who can tell them apart?
Make haste to enjoy life while you have it. Why care what happens when you are dead?

Wealth and poverty are both harmful

1

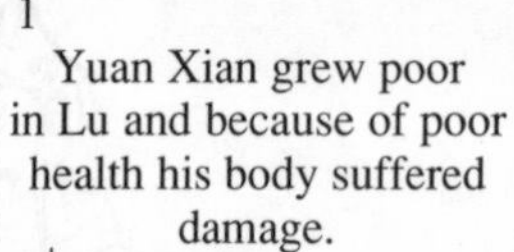

Yuan Xian grew poor in Lu and because of poor health his body suffered damage.

2

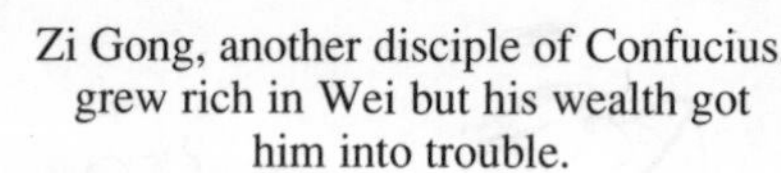

Zi Gong, another disciple of Confucius, grew rich in Wei but his wealth got him into trouble.

If that is so, wealth and poverty are both bad. Where is the right course to be found?

3

It is to be found in enjoying life, in freeing ourselves from care.

4

Hence those who are good at enjoying life are not poor, and those who are good at freeing themselves from care do not get rich.

5

One should take care of one's bodily needs and not hanker after status and wealth. Otherwise, the body is the one that suffers damage.

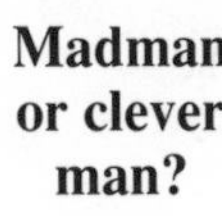

Madman or clever man?

Duanmu Shu of Wei was a rich descendant of Zi Gong. He did not bother with the issues of his time, but followed his impulse and did as he pleased.
1

2 He indulged in food, wine, women and gambling.

3 Even rare things from distant lands he would send for without fail.

4 He lived in sumptuous palaces and feasted on all kinds of delicacies.

5 He had innumerable concubines to wait on him and satisfy his desires.

6
When he travelled he always went wherever he pleased, however long and perilous the journey.
7
Every day the guests in his court were counted in hundreds.
8
Down in his kitchen the fire never went out.
The leftovers of his extravagance he distributed far and wide, first in his own clan, next in the town and villages around, and finally all over the country.
9
10
When he reached the age of sixty, and his vitality and health were beginning to wane, he let go of his family affairs and gave away all the precious things in his storehouses.

11
He gave away all his concubines and valuables. Within a year, he had given away everything, leaving nothing for his own children and grandchildren.
12
Inheritance? I have nothing to give you!
13
When he fell ill, he had no medicine in store.
14
When he died, he did not leave any money for his burial. The people throughout the whole country who had enjoyed his bounty made a collection among themselves to bury him, and restored the property of his children and grandchildren.
15
When Qin Guli heard of it, he said:
Duanmu Shu was a madman. He disgraced the disciple of Confucius who was his ancestor.
16
When Duangan Sheng heard of it, he said:
Duanmu Shu's qualities surpassed his ancestor's. All his actions astonished common people, but truly reason approves them.
Zhuang Zi advocated understanding one's inner state, whereas Yang Zhu advocated enjoying the world's offerings to the limit. So what is the purpose of living?

Living and dying
1
Meng Sunyang asked Yang Zhu:
Suppose that a man values his life and takes care of his body; can he hope by such means to prolong his life?
It is impossible to live forever.
2
Can he hope to prolong his life?
What is the point of prolonging life? Our likes and dislikes are the same now as they were of old.
3
The joys and bitterness of worldly affairs, changes of fortune, good government and discord, are the same now as they were of old. We have heard it already, seen it already, experienced it already. Even a hundred years is long enough to satiate us. Could we endure the bitterness of still longer life?
If that is so, isn't it better to die earlier rather than prolonging life?
5
No. While you are alive, resign yourself and let life run its course. Satisfy all desires and wait for death. When it is time to die, resign yourself and let death take its course. Go right to your destination, which is extinction. Be resigned to everything, let everything run its course. What need is there to delay it or speed it on its way?
If one does not cling to life or fear death, then whether life is long or short makes no difference.

Not sacrificing a hair for the world

8
It is clear that one hair is a trifle compared with skin and flesh, and skin and flesh compared with one joint.
9
However, enough hairs are worth as much as skin and flesh, enough skin and flesh as much as one joint. You cannot deny that one hair has its place among the myriad parts of the body. How can one treat it lightly?
10
I do not know how to answer you. I can only say that if you were to question Lao Zi and Guan Yin about your opinion, they would agree with you.
Cherish your body.
Yes!
11
If I were to question the Great Yu and Mo Zi, they would agree with me.
Benefit the world.
!
In ancient times there were those who would not sacrifice a single hair for the world. Even if they were offered unlimited riches, they would not give up a single hair.

The great and the trifling
1
Yang Zhu visited the king of Liang.
Ruling an empire is as simple as grasping something in the palm of one's hand.
2
You have one wife and one concubine, whom you cannot control, and a garden of three acres, which you cannot weed. Are you the person to tell me that it is so easy to rule an empire?
3
All right, I shall explain it to you. Have you seen a shepherd with his flock?
4
Send a boy with a stick on his shoulder to follow a flock of sheep, and they will go east or west as he wishes.
5
Make Yao lead one sheep, and Shun follow behind with a stick on his shoulder, and they couldn't make the sheep budge.

6
Besides, the big fish which can swallow a boat does not swim in small streams.
7
The high-flying birds do not settle in ponds and puddles.
8
The Huang Zhong and Da Lu music cannot accompany the dance in common entertainments. Why? Because the sound is far above the ordinary.
9
That is why it is said: "One who sets out on a great enterprise does not concern himself with trifles; one who achieves great successes does not achieve small ones."
A child can control a hundred sheep; Yao and Shun could not even move a single sheep, yet they rule an empire.

Empty pursuits

Yang Zhu said:
People find no rest because of four pursuits – long life, reputation, office, possessions.
Whoever has these four goals dreads spirits, fears other men, cowers before authority, and is terrified of punishment. I call him "a man in flight from things".

1

He can be killed, he can be given life;
The destiny which decides is outside him.

2

If you do not go against destiny, why should you yearn for long life? If you are not conceited about honours, why should you yearn for reputation? If you do not want power, why should you yearn for office? If you are not greedy for wealth, why should you yearn for possessions?

3

4

One who sees this I call "a man in accord with things".
Nothing in the world counters him;
The destiny which decides is within him.

One who does not aspire to attain office and power will have peace of mind and a trouble-free existence. He does not have to live in constant anxiety about worldly affairs like the kings and lords.

Simple-minded rustic
There was a peasant in Song, whose ordinary coat was of tangled hemp and it barely kept him alive through the winter.
1
2
When the spring sun rose in the east, he warmed his body in the sunshine.
3
No one knows how warm it is to bare one's back to the sun. I shall make a present of this knowledge to our ruler, and he will richly reward me.
I want to go to the capital and reveal a secret...
I advise you not to go.
4
I eat these delicious greens every day.
What an awful taste!
Once there was a man who had a taste for broad beans, nettle seeds, celery and young shoots. He recommended the dishes to some important people in his district. When they tried the dish, it stung their mouths and upset their stomachs.
5
6
They all smiled coldly and put the blame on him, and he was very embarrassed. You are just like him.
What may be acceptable fare to a poor man is something that is hard to swallow to a rich man. Habits of a lifetime cannot be changed overnight.

Explaining Conjunctions

Self and shadow
When you know how to keep to the rear, I can start teaching you about right action.
Lie Zi was studying under Hu Zi.
1
What do you mean by keeping to the rear?
2
Look round at your shadow, and you will understand.
3
When I bend and my body is crooked, so is my shadow. When my body is straight, so is my shadow.
4
So whether I want to be crooked or straight is up to my body and not my shadow.
5
So whether to bend or stand upright rests with the figure and not with the shadow; and whether we should be active or passive depends on other things and not on ourselves.
6
That is what is meant by "staying at the front by keeping to the rear". Be careful of your words, for someone will agree with them. Be careful of your conduct, for someone will imitate it.

Echo

Guan Yin told Lie Zi:
If your words are beautiful or ugly, so is their echo.
1
If your person is tall or short, so is the shadow.
2
Reputation is the echo, conduct is the shadow.
3
Therefore the sage knows what will go in by seeing what came out, knows what is coming by observing what has passed. This is the principle by which he knows in advance.
4
We judge by our experience, verify by the experience of others. If a man loves me I am sure to love him. If he hates me I am sure to hate him.
5
Similarly Tang and Wu became emperors because they loved the empire. Jie and Zhou were ruined because they hated the empire; this is the verification.
6
How others treat us depends on how we treat them. It is like a shadow - if you are upright it is also upright. Or an echo - the nature of what you said is its content.

Aim of learning the Tao
The reason for inquiring into the Way is to get rich. I can get rich by possessing treasures, so why should I need the Way?
Yen Hui said to Lie Zi:
1
Qie and Zhou gave weight to nothing but their own interests and neglected the Way; that is why they perished.
2
Men who are devoid of integrity and who live for food and nothing else, contending with others, surely they are no better than beasts?
3
If you are no better than a dog or chicken, others will not respect you. Danger and disgrace will then befall you.
4
The aim of inquiring into the Tao is to rise above human limitations and not to pursue worldly goals.

Lie Zi learns archery
1
Lie Zi was learning archery and hit bull's eye once.
2
He sought advice from Guan Yin about the secrets of archery.
Do you know why you hit bull's eye?
No.
3
It won't do yet. Practise harder.
Yes.
4
After three years of practice, Lie Zi again reported to Guan Yin.
5
Do you know what it takes to hit bull's eye?
Yes.
To hit bull's eye by chance is not good enough. One has to understand the whole process of archery to plumb its depth.
6
Good. Hold on to this knowledge and do not lose it. This applies not only to archery but to ruling the state and being master of oneself. The sage probes, not the fact of survival or ruin, but the reasons.

Foolishness and wisdom

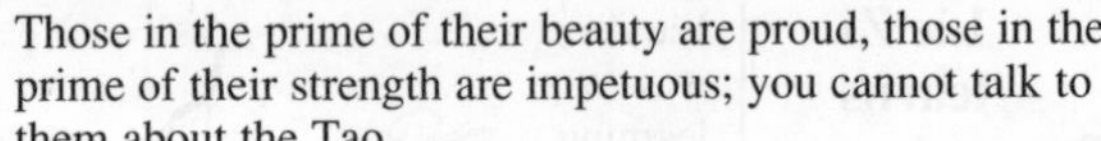

Those in the prime of their beauty are proud, those in the prime of their strength are impetuous; you cannot talk to them about the Tao.

If a man is proud or impetuous, no one tells him things.
You tell me, have I done wrong?

But if no one tells him things he is alone with no one to enlighten him.

The wise man gives responsibilities to others, and therefore his power does not diminish when he grows old and he is not thrown into confusion when his knowledge runs out.

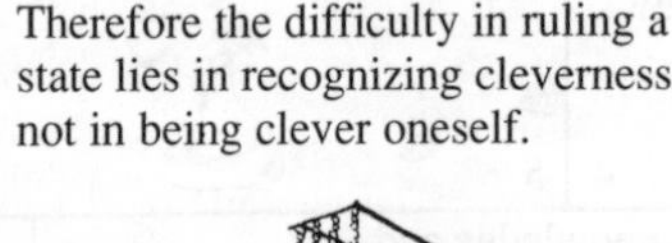

Therefore the difficulty in ruling a state lies in recognizing cleverness, not in being clever oneself.

To be proud and conceited is to block wisdom. The highest state of Tao is when intelligence acts without any self-imposed hindrance.

Trying to outdo nature

There was a man of Song who made a mulberry leaf out of a jade to give to his prince. It took him three years to finish making it. It looked just like the real thing.

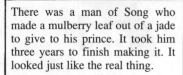

1

He presented the work of art to the prince and became famous overnight.

2

3

The man's skill won him a regular salary from the government and he lived in luxury.

4

You don't look like a tree!

Lie Zi remarked:
If heaven and earth grew things so slowly that it took them three years to finish a leaf, there would not be many things with leaves.

Thus the sage trusts the transforming process of the Tao, and puts no trust in cunning and skill.

5

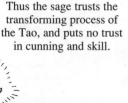

The man of Song took three years to create a leaf and made a name for himself. If a tree were to take three years to produce a leaf, it would give itself a bad name.

Foresight

Lie Zi lived in poverty in Zheng state, and his face had a starved look.
Lie Zi is known to be a man who possesses The Way. If he is in need while living in your state, may it not be thought that you are not a generous patron?
Hmm...
Despatch a gift of grain to him immediately.
Yes!
I am sorry. Please thank Chief Minister Zi Yang on my behalf. I cannot accept his grain.
We are poor and starvation shows in our faces. The Duke hears of you and sends you food, yet you refuse the gift. We must be destined to misery!
It is not that the Duke knows me personally. He sent me grain because of what another man said. If he should ever condemn me, it will also be on the word of another. I don't want to get involved with him or his affairs.
In the end it did happen that the people made trouble and killed Zi Yang.
The state of flux in Nature is not something humans can fathom. But as to worldly affairs, a man of Tao is able to see how they arise and how they will end.

A question of timing
Mr Shih of Lu had two sons; one loved learning, the other loved warfare.
1
2
The son who was a scholar presented himself as a teacher to the Marquis of Qi, who admitted him to the court as tutor to his sons.
Mr Shih's neighbour Mr Meng also had two sons, trained in the same way, but he was miserably poor.
He was envious of the wealth of the Shih family.
3
The other son went to Chu and presented himself as a strategist to the King, who was pleased with him and put him in command of the army.
4
Why are you so rich?
It's because my two sons made use of their abilities to attain high office.
5
Then one of Mr Meng's son went to Qin and presented himself to the King.
Rule with morality!
6

7
At present the princes of the states are in violent contention, and they are occupied solely with arming and feeding their troops. If I rule my state in accordance with moral teaching, this will be the way to ruin.
8
So he castrated the man and banished him.
9
The other son went to Wei, and presented himself as a strategist to the Marquis of Wei.
Rule with strategy.
10
Mine is a weak state. If I rely on military force, I will not last long.
11
The Marquis was afraid that if he let the man go, he would go to another state and cause him serious trouble. So he cut off the man's feet and sent him back to Lu.
12
How come my two sons failed and yours succeeded?
13
"Pick the right time and flourish, Miss the right time and perish." Nowhere is there a principle which is right in all circumstances, or an action that is wrong in all circumstances. The method we used yesterday we may discard today and use again in the future. There are no fixed right and wrong to decide whether we use it or not.
There are no definite right or wrong human principles. To be able to adapt them to the changing times is true wisdom.

Attack and being attacked
1
Duke Wen of Qin set out to meet his allies, intending to attack Wei.
2
Ha! Ha! Ha!
Gong Zi Chu, why do you laugh?
How are you?
Hee! Hee!
I was laughing at a neighbour of mine, who was escorting his wife on a visit to her family. He saw an attractive woman on the roadside.
3
4
Hee!
But when he looked — around at his wife, there was another man beckoning to her. I take the liberty of laughing at this.
5
I get your point. Stop the march to attack Wei, we shall go home.
He returned with his army, but before he arrived another state had attacked his northern borders.
6
One must not merely look forward to the gains one stands to make, but also consider whether there are dangers lurking behind one.

The rain that does not last
Zhao Xiang Zi sent Xinzhi Muzi to attack Di state. The general was victorious and took two major towns.
1
Our army is victorious. We have taken the towns of Cuo Ren and Zhong Ren.
Oh!
2
Sigh!
We have captured two towns in one day. That's good news. Why is Your Highness looking so grave?
3
The Changjiang and Yellow River are at high tide only for three days; stormy winds and fierce rains do not last out the morning; the sun is at high noon for less than a moment. Now I have no steady accumulation of noble deeds behind me. When two cities fall to me in a morning, ruin will surely come to me!
4
This ruler's kingdom will surely grow stronger. Worrying leads to glory, contentment leads to ruin.
When Confucius heard this he said:
5
To win is not the difficulty; the difficulty is to make victory last.

Good luck and tough luck
1
There was a vagabond from Song who performed a trick for Lord Yuan.
2
I enjoyed watching your performance. Here's a present of gold and silk for you.
Thank you!
3
There was another vagabond who could also perform acrobatic feats and he presented himself to Lord Yuan to give a performance.
Not long ago there was a man who came to me with an extraordinary trick. There was no point in the trick, but I happened to be in a good mood then, so I gave him a present of gold and silk. You must have come because you heard about it and want a reward too.
4
5
The acrobat was detained for a month.
The two vagabonds have similar skills but their fates were different. This shows the importance of being at the right place at the right time.
Things are always in a state of flux, and as circumstances change, so do human reactions.
6

Horse sense

Aged Bo Le was very adept at finding horses for Duke Mu of Qin.
It's really not easy to find someone as capable as you. Is there anyone you know who can take over from you?
1
This man here, Jiu Fang Gao, collects firewood for me. As a judge of horses, he is my equal.
That's wonderful. Ask him to find me a fleet-footed horse.
2
After three months, Jiu Fang Gao finally found a suitable horse.
3
In Sha Qiu, I spotted a very good horse.
Wonderful! What kind of a horse is it?
4
It's a yellow mare.
I want to take a look at it.
5

6
When the Duke saw the horse, it turned out to be a black stallion.
7
He's no good, the fellow you sent to find horses. What does he know about horses?
8
So now he has risen to this! He is worth ten thousand any number of people like me.
9
What he observes is the innermost impulse behind the horse's movements. He grasps the essence and forgets the form. That is why he could not remember the colour and sex.
Huh?
10
The animal later proved itself to be a great horse.
A man of Tao concerns himself with the essence of things and not their appearances. For example, young men usually only notice a girl's appearance; it takes an old man to evaluate her virtues. Right?

The higher you go, the harder you fall

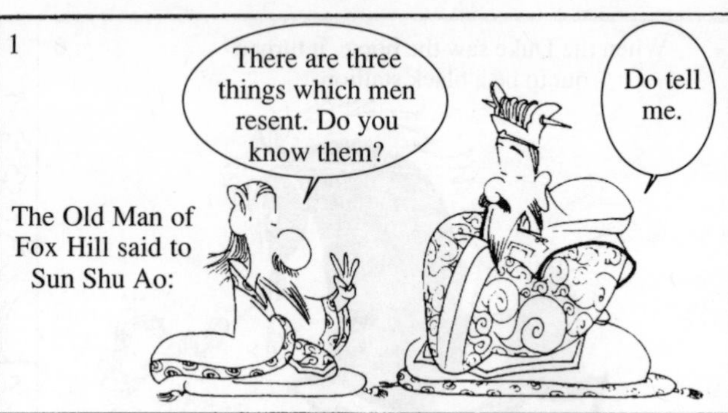

1
The Old Man of Fox Hill said to Sun Shu Ao:
There are three things which men resent. Do you know them?
Do tell me.

If your rank is high, others will envy you. If your office is great, your prince will hate you. If your salary is large, there will always be resentment.
2

The higher the rank, the more humble I am. The greater my office, the more meticulous I shall be. The larger my salary, the more generous I will be. Acting like this, may I avoid the three causes of resentment?
3

After my death, the king will offer you a fief. Be sure not to accept strategically useful land. There is a strategically useless land with the inauspicious name of Graveyard Hill. This is the only place which can be owned for long.
When Sun Shu Ao was on his death-bed, he told his son:
4

When Sun Shu Ao died, the king did offer to enfief his son an excellent plot of land. The son made excuses and did not accept it, asking for Graveyard Hill. It was given to him, and the family has not lost it yet.
5

Many grand things in the world do not endure. Keep away from contentious situations to preserve your well-being.

Death of two fools

7
8
A man of Yan who heard about it called together his clansmen and warned them:
If you meet with robbers, don't be like that smart aleck Niu Que.
Soon afterwards his younger brother went to Qin.
9
!
Friend, pay the road toll!
10
If I let them rob me, I will suffer the same fate as Niu Que.
11
Try and rob me if you can. Take that!
One against three, you can't win.
12

Wah!
Ha! Ha!
13
Return me my clothes and money!
15
Don't go away! Please return my things to me!
!
14
Sparing your life was generosity enough, and now you won't stop running after us.
16
Similar actions won't reap similar results. One should act in accordance with the needs of the situation and not try to force a certain outcome.
17
Once a man turns robber, what room has he for kindness? Now you die!

The unlucky gambler
Mr Yu, a rich man of Liang, was fond of gambling. He was playing backgammon with some friends when ...
1
Oops!
2
3
A bird flying outside the window dropped a dead rat on a group of mercenaries below and it struck the head of their leader.
4
How dare that rich bastard throw a dead rat at me!
One night, the mercenaries went to Mr Yu's house and wiped out his entire family.
5
The twists and turns of fate often result in tragedy. Mr Yu, for all his wealth, died needlessly.

Refusing a criminal's food
1
There was a man named Yuan Xingmu. He was travelling and collapsed from hunger.
2
3
4
Who are you?
I am Qiu of Hufu.
5
What? Aren't you a criminal? What do you mean by giving me food?
I am a respectable man. I will not eat your food.
Phui!
6
He pressed both hands against the ground to vomit it out, but it stuck gurgling in his throat.
Then he flopped on his face and died.
Serves you right!
7
The man from Hufu was a criminal, but there was nothing criminal about the food. To call food criminal and refuse to eat it because the man who offers it is a criminal is to confuse the name with the reality.

Past caring about death
1
Chu Lishu was in the service of Duke Ao of Zhu.
2
Feeling that the duke did not appreciate him, he went away and lived on the seashore. But when the duke was in trouble, he took leave of his friends and went to fight to the death for him.
3
Duke Ao is trouble. I am going to sacrifice my life for him.
4
You felt that the duke did not appreciate you and that is why you left him. If you go and die for him now, it will make no difference whether he appreciated you or not.
5
Not at all. I left because I felt that he did not appreciate me; and to die for him now will prove that he did not appreciate me.
I shall die for him in order to shame the lords of future generations who do not appreciate their vassals.
6
We may call Chu Lishu a man who carried resentment to the point of no longer caring for his own life.

Yang Bu
beats the dog
Yang Zhu's younger brother Yang Bu went out wearing a white silk coat.
1
It rained, and he took off the white coat and came back dressed in black.
2
His dog did not recognize him and barked when it came out to greet him.
3
4
Insolent dog!
5
Stop beating it.
This stupid dog didn't recognize me.
6
You are no different yourself. Supposing that just now your dog had gone out white and come back black, wouldn't you have been surprised?
To be overly concerned about the form will cause one to forget the essence. Status, power and wealth often cause one to forget oneself.

Life and immortality

1
There was a man who claimed he knew the Way to become immortal.
2
The Lord of Yan came to know about the man and sent a messenger to fetch him.
3
4
I am too late. He has died.
5
Idiot! Drag him out and execute him.
Your Highness! Spare my life!
6
None of a man's cares is more urgent than death, and there is nothing that he values more than his life. That recluse has lost his own life, how could he have made you immortal?
7
What you say is true. All right, I will spare your life.
The minister was also wrong. He who knows about immortality may not necessarily be able to apply it.

Charity or cruelty?

1
The people of Handan presented doves to Zhao Qianzi, Minister to Duke Ding of Qin, on New Year's Day morning. He was delighted and richly rewarded them.
Why do the people present doves to you?
Ho! Ho!
2
3
We release living things on New Year's Day as a gesture of compassion.
The people know you wish to release them, so they vie with each other to catch them, and many of the doves die. If you wish to keep them alive, it would be better to forbid the people to catch them. When you release doves after catching them, the compassion does not make up for the mistake.
There is truth in what you say. I will follow your advice.
4
When there is the motive to be virtuous, there is no virtue. To capture the doves and then release them not only cannot atone for the sin, but actually makes it worse for the cycle is kept going.

The strong eating the weak

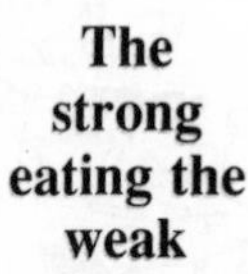
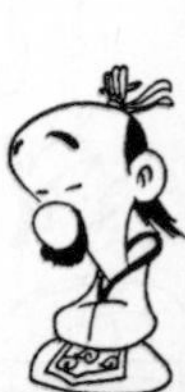

1
Tian of Qi was going on a journey. He sacrificed in his courtyard to the god of the roads and banqueted a thousand guests. Someone was serving fish and geese at the seat of honour. Tian looked at them and remarked:
How generous heaven is to humanity! It grows the five grains and breeds the fishes and birds for humans!
True!
Yes!
Right!
Yes!

2
It is not as Your Lordship says. The myriad things between heaven and earth, born in the same way as we are, do not differ from us in kind.
!

3
One kind is no nobler than the other. It is simply that the stronger and cleverer rule the weaker and sillier. Things take it in turns to eat each other, but they are not bred for each other's sake. Men take the things which are edible and eat them, but how can it be claimed that heaven bred them originally for the sake of man?

4
Besides, mosquitoes and gnats bite our skin, tigers and wolves eat our flesh. Did heaven originally breed man for the sake of mosquitoes and gnats, tigers and wolves?
Er...
All the things of creation come from the same source and live together in this world. The difference is only in the form and there is no difference in worth. We are all just constituents in Nature's immensity.

Disgrace

1
There was a poor man in Qi who always begged in the city market.
Thank you!
2
The crowd in the market got tired of seeing him so often, and no one would give him anything.
!!!
3
So he went to the stables of the Tian family, and made a living as a cleaner.
4
Don't you think it is a disgrace to be a cleaner in the stables?
5
There is nothing in the world more disgraceful than to beg. If even begging did not disgrace me, how can I be disgraced by being a cleaner in the stables?
!
Disgrace or no disgrace, it is all in the mind.

Empty wealth
1
There was a man of Song who picked up an invalid bank promissory note.
2
Wow! Twenty thousand taels of silver!
3
I am now a rich man!
20万两
12月31日还
4
Heh! Heh!
5
Heh! Heh!
6
Heh! Heh!
7
Heh! Heh!
Why are you behaving so high and mighty?
8
Show some respect when you speak to me! I am now a man of means!
Wealth or no wealth, it is all in the mind.

Evil designs
1
There was a man who owned a withered wu-tong tree. His neighbour said that a withered wu-tong tree was unlucky.
It is a sign of ill omen to have a withered wu-tong tree. Chop it down!
Is that so?
2
This man is very kind. He was worried I might have a spell of bad luck.
3
You might as well give me some of it to use as firewood?
4
So in reality you wanted to get free firewood. That was why you asked me to cut down the tree. How devious you are!
You've wronged me! I never had such intentions!
Was the neighbour devious? It was all in the man's mind.

Evil
thoughts
1
There was a man who lost his axe and suspected the boy next door of stealing it.
He watched the boy. The man thought: his expression, his behaviour, everything about him betrayed that he had stolen the axe.
2
Everything shows that he is the thief. No doubt about it!
3
Later, he found the axe behind his own house.
Ah! Actually it's me who forgot where I had left it.
4
On another day, he saw the boy again. Nothing in the boy's manner suggested that he would steal an axe.
Whether the boy looked like a thief or not, it was all in the man's mind.
5

Thoughts of rebellion
1
The Duke of Bai was contemplating rebellion against his ruler.
2
Coming out of the court, he stood leaning on his horse-goad, without remembering to hold it the right way up.
3
The sharp end poked his cheek.
4
The blood spilled on the ground, but he did not notice it.
5
If a man forgets his own head, is there anything he will not forget?
When the man of Zheng heard of the incident, he remarked:
When one's heart is occupied with cares, he would stumble over a pit and knock against a tree, and yet not realize it.

Tunnel vision
1
Once there was a man of Qi who was obsessed with gold.
2
3
He went to the stall of a goldsmith.
4
He snatched the gold and fled.
Stop the thief!
5
Lawmen caught up with him.
6
Why did you snatch someone's gold in front of so many people?
7
8
At the time when I took it, I did not see the people. I only saw the gold.
When one's mind is preoccupied with something, he would forget about other things. But to pay no attention to things around one is extremely dangerous.

《亚太漫画系列》

御风而行的哲思

列子说

编著：蔡志忠
翻译：许国强

亚太图书（新）有限公司出版